STACCATO SCRIPTS

TRAFFORD TANZI

Claire Luckham

Series Editors/Support Material:
Kate Harris and John Mannion

Stanley Thornes (Publishers) Ltd

First published in 1991 by:
Stanley Thornes (Publishers) Ltd
Old Station Drive
Leckhampton
CHELTENHAM GL53 0DN
England

British Library Cataloguing in Publication Data

Luckham, Claire
    Trafford Tanzi. – (Staccato scripts)
    I. Title   II. Series
    822

ISBN 0-7487-1167-8

Typeset by Tech-Set, Gateshead Tyne & Wear
Printed and bound in Great Britain at Ebenezer Baylis & Son Ltd
The Trinity Press, Worcester, and London

ACKNOWLEDGEMENTS

The authors and publishers are grateful to the following for their permission to reproduce photographs and extracts.

All-Sport UK Ltd page 50 • 'Very Simply Topping Up The Brake Fluid', Simon Armitage from *Zoom*, reprinted by permission of Bloodaxe Books Ltd, 1989 page 55 • *Acting and Stagecraft Made Simple* (adapted), Derek Bowskill pages 38-9 • 'All My Friends Are Married Now', Barbara Child from *Clearly Seen*, Quartet Books, page 56 • The Dukes Theatre pages 33, 35, 46-7 • *Things We Do*, Ladybird Books Ltd, 1964 page 44 • *Lancashire Evening Post* page 48 • *MATCH* page 45 • *North-West Evening Mail* page 48 • *The Observer*, 23 September 1990 page 51 • Glenys Roberts page 53 • 'I Had Rather Be A Woman', Daphne Schiller page 54 • *The Visitor* page 49.

Lyrics *Stand by Your Man* © 1968, Al Gallico Music Corp, USA. Reproduced by permission of EMI Music Publishing Ltd, London WC2H 0EA page 20.

Cover photograph from the 1984 Leeds Playhouse production, used with the kind permission of the West Yorkshire Playhouse, Leeds. Photograph by Simon Warner.

Every effort was made to contact copyright holders and the publishers apologise if any have been overlooked.

CONTENTS

CHARACTERS

Referee
Tanzi's Mum
Tanzi's Dad
Platinum Sue
Dean Rebel
Trafford Tanzi
Dr Grope, a school psychiatrist (played by the **Referee**)

When staging the production, at least one musician will also be required. This could be a pianist or, better, an electronic keyboard player. Local repertory theatres which have staged the play may be able to loan backing tapes, etc.

Act one

*The wrestling ring. The audience should be able to purchase drinks at reasonable prices. The piano player vamps a few requests. The **Referee** climbs into the ring and takes a microphone from one of the corner posts. He uses it for all official announcements.*

Referee Gentlemen, gentlemen; ladies and gentlemen; top of the bill tonight Contact Promotions proudly present, for the first time in any wrestling ring, a man and a woman fighting to the finish. The woman, ladies and gentlemen, is the reigning European Ladies Champion, Trafford Tanzi. The man, the ever-popular Dean Rebel. Stay in your seats for the fight of the decade.

But first, to commemorate this great occasion, ladies and gentlemen, have you ever asked yourselves what it takes to become a champion? Are they born or are they bred? How did Trafford Tanzi happen upon her speciality hold, the Venus Flytrap? In ten dazzling rounds Contact Promotions present the exclusive Trafford Tanzi story. Told, ladies and gentlemen, with the help of members of the wrestling fraternity.

(Music: Entry of the Gladiators. The cast take a fast bow in character as their names are called)

Referee Allow me to introduce to you, that lucky lady, Tanzi's Mum. Tanzi's Dad. All the world loves a villain – only joking, only joking. Her friend and confidante, Platinum Sue. The man who taught her so much: Dean Rebel. And the little lady herself, the reigning European champion: Trafford Tanzi. The music tonight is provided at very short notice by Theolonius Monks and his electric upright. All the other parts will be played by my good self.

(Music finishes)

Referee Ladies and gentlemen, the Trafford Tanzi Story. See Tanzi grow from nappies to netball. Watch her fall in love, discover the harsh realities of the wrestling world, invent that deadly hold the Venus Flytrap. See her use it to destroy her enemies as she climbs to the top of her profession. The Trafford Tanzi Story, her hopes, her fears, her early years. Can I have the contestants for Round One?

(**Tanzi** *and* **Mum** *go to their corners*)

Referee   In the red corner, ladies and gentlemen: Trafford Tanzi. There she is, and she's just toddling. She's one year old. A baby.

(**Tanzi** *falls over and goos*)

Referee   In the blue corner, her opponent for Round One, her mum, a mum in a million. Seconds away, Round One.

(*Bell*)

Mum   Come here, Come on, come here. Tan-zi. (**Tanzi** *totters over to her*) Mummy's little girlie. (**Mum** *pushes her over*) Tanzi were always a disappointment to me. (*She takes the mike as* **Tanzi** *clambers to her feet again*)

I wanted a boy, (*'Head mares'* **Tanzi**)
I wanted a lad,
I wanted a boy, (*Another 'head mare'*)
And so did her Dad.

When you first have a thought like maybe,
I just might be having a baby,
You don't just stand at the sink, thinking
Pink, pink, pink, pink, pink.
No, you sit on the loo, cooing,
Blue, blue, blue,
For a boy because boys are important,
And when he does things that he oughtn't,
Well, I know it's very silly,
But you smile and you forgive him cos you know,
One day he'll grow
Into a man.

(*Spoken over instrumental, while ogling the* **Referee**)

And men are wonderful, aren't they? They're strong and clever and decisive and they can do things and talk about things and they give me goose pimples just thinking about them and . . .

(**Tanzi** *comes between her and the* **Referee**)

Mum   I wanted a boy, (*'Head mare'*)
And look what I got,
Well I got a girl, (*'Head mare'*)
All covered in snot.

And when at last the stork comes calling,
And his bundle is pink – appalling!
You lie there feeling low, going,
No, no, no, no, no.

And then you have a little cry, sighing,
Why? Why? Why?

Cos a boy is for adoring.
But a girl is just plain boring,
Unless she's very pretty,
Which she isn't more's the pity,
And you can't forgive her cos you know,
She'll never grow
Into a man.

(*Spoken as before*) And men are wonderful, aren't they? I
mean they tell you what to do, and how to do it, and when
they've got any left they give you housekeeping money
and . . . oh Tanzi! (**Tanzi** *has come between the* **Referee** *and*
Mum *with an interesting 'nose dropping'*) I wanted a boy,
frock! (*She takes a frock from* **Sue** *and dresses* **Tanzi** *through
the next*)

To dress all in blue,
What use is a girl?
Well, what can she *do*?

(**Tanzi** *dribbles over the ropes through this next*)

Mum	Ah that's better, nothing like real nylon. She almost does me credit. The trouble I took with her. The white oh-so-white matinée jackets. The frilly knickers. Little frocks with 'Tanzi' sewn on them in pink silk. Nothing was too much trouble in them days. Oh, it seems a shame to hit her.
Referee	Right, no contest. No contest.
Musician	Oh no! (*He has been dribbled on*)
Mum	No, wait a minute – you're not dribbling, are you, child? Are you? Would you credit it! All down her dress with pink motif. (*She 'posts'* **Tanzi. Tanzi** *falls*) Can I have her din-dins please? (**Referee** *hands her a large tin of baby food and a spoon.* **Tanzi** *gets excited*) Now Tanzi, wait. Wait till you've got your bib on. Bib on first. (**Sue** *hands* **Mum** *the bib.* **Tanzi** *complains.* **Mum** *punches her in the stomach.* **Tanzi** *falls*)
Referee	Hey, you didn't use your fist, did you, missus? I have to ask.
Mum	Did you see me use me fist?
Referee	Er . . . no. No, carry on. (**Tanzi** *is crying*)
Mum	Tanzi. Tanzi, oo-oo! Mummy's little girlie. Din-dins. Nicey nicey foo-ood. Open mouth for Mummy, there's a good girl. (**Tanzi** *opens her mouth.* **Mum** *puts food in. It's horrible*) Good girl, three more mouthfuls and we're finished.

(**Tanzi** *shakes her head. She grabs the tin and spits the food back in. She takes a handful and likes the feel of it. She smears it on her face. Then another on* **Mum**'s *face. Then one on the* **Referee**'s. *Then starts throwing it at the audience*)

Mum   Look at her. Look at her. Spoilt brat. Tanzi. Tanzi! Tanzi doesn't love her Mummy no more. Tanzi, Mummy's got sweeties for you. Sweeties. (*To the audience*) Haven't you got any paper you can rustle? Sweeties! (**Tanzi** *approaches*) Come along Tanzi, there's a good girl. Food; sweeties. (**Tanzi** *hands over the tin*) Ta. (**Mum** *takes the tin with one hand and 'Irish whips'* **Tanzi** *with the other*) Oooh, look at her! The dirty little girl. (*She puts an 'ankle lock' on her and twists through this next*) Tanzi doesn't love her Mummy no more. The nasty, dirty, little girl. (*'Step-over leglock' and 'stamp'*. **Tanzi** *bursts into tears*)

(*Bell*)

Referee   Ladies and gentlemen: the winner in Round One, Mum. A big hand for Mum please, showing us all how to do it. Thank you.

(**Mum** *takes a bow and then sweeps up the food during this next*)

Referee   Round Two. Can I have the contestants for Round Two please? In the red corner, Trafford Tanzi. In the blue corner, Platinum Sue. Girls, come here.

(*They come to the centre, the* **Referee** *turns his back on* **Tanzi** *and chats up* **Sue**)

Referee   Now listen, I want nothing you're going to be ashamed of after. No scratching, hair pulling, biting, agreed?

Sue   Yes, Mr Referee.

Referee   Good girl.

Tanzi   Aren't you gonna ask me then?

Referee   Yeah, when you can wriggle your backside like that. Tanzi is at school. She's six years old. Just six. Seconds away, Round Two.

(*Bell*)

(**Tanzi** *holds her hand out to shake hands.* **Sue** *takes it down to the ground and stamps on it*)

Tanzi   Fwaugh, fwaugh.

(**Tanzi** *returns to corner, comes back with a lollipop. She offers it to* **Sue**. **Sue** *takes it and 'Irish whips' her.* **Tanzi** *gets up.* **Sue** *points in the air.* **Tanzi** *looks up.* **Sue** *'claims' her leg.* **Tanzi** *break falls*)

Referee   One . . . er . . . two . . . er . . . three . . . er . . .

Sue One, two-oo, three-ee,
Tanzi hit rock bottom,
She tried to knock the champion out,
But found her chance was rotten.

Tanzi Why can't we be friends? I want to be friends.

Sue Because we can't.

Tanzi But why?

Sue Me Mam says we can't, so there. You've got a snotty nose and dirty knees. You're a tom boy. Only play boys' games. I play house and all the girls' games. You're a slut, so there.

Tanzi I will play if you want.

Sue I can't. Your mouth's dirty.

Tanzi It's not.

Sue You swear.

Tanzi I don't.

Sue You do.

Tanzi Don't.

Sue Do.

Tanzi Don't.

Sue Do.

Tanzi Well, what do I say then?

Sue I don't know. But me Mam says you do, so there.

Tanzi Well, what's swearing then?

Sue Well . . . dirty words.

Tanzi You don't kno-ow, you don't kno-ow.

Sue I do. I do. I do.

Tanzi I do because me Mam tells me Dad not to, so there.

Sue Oo, what's he say? Go on. Tell us.

Tanzi Promise to be friends?

Sue I might. Yes. Go on. Go on.

Tanzi Well, in the morning when he can't find his socks he says, 'Bloody Hell!'

Sue Ooh!

(They both run round the ring yelling, 'Bloody Hell' and 'Poo-poo-poo' etc.)

Tanzi   And I know that's swearing cos me Mam tells me Dad to
stop bloody swearing.

Sue   Oo! Oo! Bloody Hell! Bloody swearing!

(*They play pat-a-cake through this next*)

Sue *and* **Tanzi**   Salami, salami,
All the boys is barmy,
Sla-ate, sla-ate,
All the girls is grea-eat!

(**Tanzi** *slaps the* **Referee** *on the last one*)

Tanzi   'ey, 'ey, 'ey, we could have a gang.

Sue   What for?

Tanzi   Fighting the boys.

Sue   Girls don't fight, me Mam says so.

Dean   (*Outside the ring*) That's it, you tell her, Sue.

Sue   Ooh! Ooh! I will! I'll tell on her. I'll tell our Miss on you.
You've been swearing.

Tanzi   But . . . but we're friends, you said.

Sue   I can't. Me Mam says I can't. And, and Miss'll send you up
to Head Miss and you'll get the slipper for fighting and
swearing, so there.

(**Tanzi** *tries not to cry. She grabs a dolly off* **Sue** *and pulls its arms and legs off and
stamps on it*)

Sue   She's got my dolly! She's got my dolly!

Referee   Now, Miss, calm down, calm down . . .

(*Bell*)

Referee   The bell's gone. Round Two to Platinum Sue.

Sue   Piece of cake. (**Sue** *climbs out of the ring*)

Referee   And as for you, my girl, watch it, or I'll have to issue you
with a public warning. You wash your mouth out with soap
and water, we want none of that filthy language in . . .

(**Tanzi** *has been swilling her mouth round. She spits the contents onto the* **Referee**)

Referee   You . . . you . . .

Dad   No, no. You're getting it all wrong. She's getting it all
wrong. My little girl wasn't like that at all. She was, she was
(*He takes the mike*) beautiful.

(**Mum** *plays violin and the* **Referee** *dons a pair of headphones and reads*
Sporting Life *as* **Dad** *sings*)

Dad   Tanzi, Tanzi: Buttercups and Tanzi,
She was so beautiful as she grew;
Little frocks and cotton socks, pretty as a chocolate box,
My little girl with her eyes of blue.

Now Daddy's got a great big thirsty,
Daddy's mouthie's very dry,
Tanzi fetch your Mummy's pursie,
Needn't tell her why.
Daddy take the funny money,
Tanzi put the purse back,
Put that ruddy purse back, Tanzi,
Do you want a smack?

Tanzi, Tanzi: Buttercups and Tanzi,
She was so beautiful as she grew;
Little frocks and cotton socks, pretty as a chocolate box,
My little girl with her eyes of blue.

Now Tanzi sit on Daddy's knee-knee
Bless her little cotton socks,
Daddy's backed a little gee-gee, on the goggle box
Tanzi make her Daddy lucky,
See his little horsey run.
Bloody hell it's going backwards,
Now look what you've done.

Tanzi, Tanzi: Buttercups and Tanzi,
She was so beautiful as she grew;
Little frocks and cotton socks, pretty as a chocolate box,
My little girl with her eyes of blue.

Referee   Thank you, thank you, Tanzi's Dad. Ladies and gentlemen,
Round Three. Tanzi meets the school psychiatrist. In the
red corner Trafford Tanzi. She is now eleven, she's eleven
years old. In the blue corner . . . oh, excuse me, it's me.

(*He hands the mike to* **Mum** *and hastily changes into* **Dr Grope. Sue** *assists,
dressed as a nurse*)

Mum   In the blue corner, the school psychiatrist, Doctor Grope,
Seconds away . . . Round Three.

(*Bell*)

(**Grope** *gets* **Tanzi** *in a 'head lock'*)

Grope   Aha. Got you. Name?

Tanzi   What?

Grope   Name, stupid. What's yours?

Tanzi   Tanzi.

Grope   Tanzi what? (*Stamp*)

Tanzi   Tanzi.

Grope   Yes, but Tanzi what? (*Stamp*) Your second name. (*He turns her away from* **Mum** *who is reffing for this round and gouges her eye*) I've got to send in a psychiatrist's report – (*Runs her face along the top rope*) – on why Tanzi whatever your name is, can't read. (*He stamps again and drops her on the floor*)

Tanzi   Green.

Grope   (*Putting his knee in her back and pulling her up by her cheek*) I should think you are.

Tanzi   That's me name.

Grope   (*Changes to a 'nerve hold' and brings her to her feet*) Oho, how green was my valley eh?

Dad   (*Outside the ring*) Stop him love, that's our name too.

Mum   Shush.

Grope   (*Walking her across the ring with 'nerve hold'*) Joke, girl. Laugh. (*Tightens hold:* **Tanzi** *screams*) Haven't you got a sense of humour? No greens is good greens, what? I never used to like my greens at school either. (**Tanzi** *breaks free and takes a swing at him. He grabs her lower lip and forces her up on tiptoe*) Temper, temper. Naughty, naughty. We're never going to find out why you don't read if you carry on like this. Right. (*He signals for* **Sue** *to hold up a reading card which has a daft picture and 'Jane helps Mum wash the dishes,' written underneath.* **Grope** *changes back to 'nerve grip'*) I'd like you to look at this card. Now what do you see? (*Applies pressure*)

Tanzi   (*Shrieks*) A girl . . .

Grope   Yes. And what is the girl called? (*Pressure*)

Tanzi   Jane. Jane . . . Jane. Jane.

Grope   Quite right. Good, very good. Mustn't stint on the praise. (*He pats her on the head and then 'rabbit punches' her to her knees*) Now Tanzi, pay attention, what's the next word? (*'Nerve hold' and pressure*)

Tanzi   Helps. Helps. Helps. Helps.

Grope   Very, very good. Now . . . (*Pressure*)

Tanzi   Mum!

Grope   Oh, did you hear that? I'm beginning to wonder if they've sent me the right girl. Let's have a look at your teeth. (*He* *forces her mouth open*) Never mind. (*He takes her nose and lifts her to her feet by it*) Now Tanzi, I want you to be a clever girl and do all the rest in one go. (*He slaps the hand holding her nose*) Come on, don't be shy.

Tanzi (*Reads*) Dig For Gold.

Grope Excellent, I . . . what? Wait a minute. (*He reads*) Wash the dishes. What did you say? Say it for me.

Tanzi Dig for Gold. (*She 'Irish whips' him*) Discover the source of the Nile. Fly to the Moon. (*'Monkey climb' on him*) That's it, that's what Jane helps her Mummy to do. Take meteoric readings of the stars.

(*She throws him at the ropes and attempts a 'tomahawk chop' as he comes off them but he 'grope ducks' and puts 'nerve hold' back on her*)

Grope Now then, my girl, I can see that we've got some learning to do.

(*He changes the hold to a 'headlock' and throttles her with his left hand*)

Dad (*Outside the ring*) Mum, mum, he's got her by the throat. (**Grope** *changes hold*)

Mum Are you choking her?

Grope Would I? I'm the school psychiatrist, I'm just teaching her to read. (*He starts throttling her again*)

Tanzi No, ow, yes, Jane Helps Mum (*Bell*) Wash The Dishes.

Grope (*Throwing her down and stamping on her*) Ja, ja, that is right, Jane help Mum vash ze dishes. Oh. (*He changes back to the* **Referee**)

Mum The winner in Round Three. Doctor Grope.

Dad (*Climbing into the ring*) You know what you are, don't you?

Grope Jealous, are we?

Dad A bleeding great bully.

Mum Break it up, break it up. My husband was always supporting Tanzi. Until she came home from school one time.

Tanzi Mum . . .

Mum She says . . .

Tanzi Can I have a career?

Mum Well! I thought . . . I'll let her Dad sort it out.

Referee Ladies and gentlemen, Round Four. Tanzi is sweet sixteen. (*He wiggles his hips,* **Tanzi** *wolf whistles*) Watch it, you. In the blue corner – watch you don't let her get away with anything – Tanzi's Dad.

Tanzi   Come on, you great pudding, you're holding up the action.

Dad   Action, did you say? She wants some action. I'll give you action and all. Ready?

Referee   Seconds away, Round Four.

(*Bell*)

Dad   (*As they circle*) You're late, where've you been?

Tanzi   Same as every night, at school . . .

(*They change direction*)

Dad   Answer me, my girl, I haven't come back early from the pub to hear you say at school. Come on, out with it.

(**Referee**'s *hold*)

Tanzi   It's the truth . . .

Dad   (*Puts* **Tanzi** *in a 'backhammer'*) Pull the other one. I'm . . .

Tanzi   (*Reverses 'backhammer' on him*) Listen. I can't work here because me Mam . . .

Dad   (*Putting a reverse 'backhammer' on* **Tanzi**) Has the telly on all the time and you can't concentrate. I've heard it all before. (*He stamps and forces it higher*)

Tanzi   It's true.

Dad   (*Forcing her down onto the floor through this*) I'll tell you whether it's true or not, my girl. You can't pull the wool over my eyes like you can your poor old Mum. Do you hear me? (*He stamps on her elbow*) A career!

Tanzi   But Dad . . .

Dad   And don't you 'but Dad' me either. I know where you've been going after school, don't think I don't. Girls! (*'Crutch hold' and lifts her up into an 'aeroplane spin'*) What else is there for them to do except go sneaking around in the dark with the lads. Disgusting, I call it. Makes me all hot inside thinking about it. In the back alleys, round the back of the garages. On the railway banks. Never mind they give you those badges: 'I don't play on the railway'. No. But we do, don't we? (**Dad** *has overdone the 'spin' and now staggers to his knees*) I've seen you waiting behind Oxford Road Station and . . .

(*He throws her off with a 'body slam', retreats into a corner and splashes.* **Tanzi** *rolls out from under it.* **Dad** *lies prone*)

Dad   Ooh-er . . . Tanzi . . . how can you do it to your poor old Dad.

Tanzi   (*Going to him*) Dad, Dad, I didn't mean to upset you.

Dad   (*Grabbing her foot and bringing her down. 'Ankle lock'*) There, I knew it! Filth. You've been having filth.

Tanzi   No, no, Dad.

Dad   (*Applying pressure to various 'leglocks'*) Say 'yes', will you, girl? Say yes and put me out of me misery. Tell you what, say yes and I'll forget all about you wanting a career. Right? Give you fifty quid. Fifty notes, to spend on yourself. Get the lot. Nice outfit, make-up. Get yourself a decent feller. One that'll want to marry you, not fiddle about with you up them back alleys. Come on. It's all your Mum and Dad ever wanted.

Tanzi   But it would be the same as up them alleys except I'd be married. (*She tries to raise her head through this next but* **Dad** *keeps slamming it back*) I don't want to get married. (*Slam*) I want me independence. (*Slam*) I want to be somebody! (*Slam*)

Dad   Somebody! A slut, the way you're going on. A wife is somebody, isn't she? Are you saying your mother isn't somebody? Somebody? Marriage is the best career money can buy.

Tanzi   I want some exams.

Dad   (*Trying to turn her over into a 'Boston crab'*) Filthy bits of paper! Right! You want exams. You pay for 'em. (*'Boston crab'*) You earn your own living. See how you like that. (*He sits back*)

Referee   Do you submit?

Tanzi   Yes, yes, yes.

(*Bell.* **Dad** *gets off and parades.* **Tanzi** *bursts into tears*)

Referee   In Round Four, a submission to Dad by means of a Boston crab. Come on Tanzi, oh not the waterworks for God's sake, quick, quick, can I have the contestants for Round Five please. Tanzi is now luscious eighteen and working down the local chippy. In the blue corner, the ever-popular, Dean Rebel!

(**Dean**'s *music: heavy rock. He comes through the audience signing autographs and kissing impressionable women, vaults into the ring and combs his hair*)

Referee   Seconds away, Round Five.

(*Bell*)

Tanzi   (*In the red corner still crying*) Ye-es.

Dean   Liver dinner for one with chips, rice, peas, meat and potato pie, a sausage and a pancake roll. Oh and stick a bit of fish in to round it off.

(**Tanzi** *sobs loudly.* **Dean** *does a flash 'roll' across the ring and comes up on the ropes beside her*)

Dean   What's the matter, lady? You're crying over the fish, I mean, I'm not fussy but I don't go for too much salt with it. Come on, cheer up, it might never happen. Here, wanna use me hanky? (*He removes it slowly from his trunks*) You know I don't like to see a girl crying. You take it.

Tanzi   No-o.

Dean   All right. I'll do it for yer. Come on, come here. (*She does so*) Better? (**Tanzi** *nods*) Hey-eye, you've got nice eyes. No, really you have. Much too good to waste frying chips. I mean, what did they ever know about love? Here, I'll just put me hanky away. (*Back in trunks*) Bit of a tight fit, what with the three piece suite. Hey, now you're not telling me you didn't know what we kept hidden away down there?

Referee   Watch your mouth, Rebel.

Dean   Don't be nosey. (*'Nose mares' him*) Feelin' better? Hey, that's better and better. I mean, I could see you was tasty but not well, delicious. What's yer name?

Tanzi   Tanzi.

(**Dean** *holds out his hand. She takes it. He throws her into the ropes and clinches with her as she bounces back*)

Dean   Hi, Tanzi.

Tanzi   Hi.

Dean   Don't bother to wrap yerself up, I'll eat you now.

Tanzi   Not too close, Rebel. Is that your name?

Dean   Yeah. (*He puts a 'backhammer' on her*) Dean Rebel; I'm in training to be a professional wrestler. (*He throws her to the ropes again. This time she hangs on*) Come over here and try me folding body press.

Tanzi   No.

Dean   I can see it's time for a touch of the old romance. (*He produces a bunch of flowers from his trunks*) Flowers, for the one I love.

Dad (*Outside the ring*) That's the ticket.

Tanzi Flowers! D'you think I'm soft or something. Go give 'em to your old lady.

(*She kicks them out of his hand. The* **Referee** *catches them.* **Dean** *falls back and does a 'neck spring' onto his feet again*)

Dean Well, vinegar as well! (*He takes the mike*) You're a cracker, Tanzi, we were made for each other.

(**Dean** *sings and jives with* **Tanzi** *whilst the rest of the cast forms a backing group*)

Dean Tanzi, Tanzi, you're so sweet,
Pansies couldn't grow so neat,
You're the apple of my eye,
Come on pretty baby let me hold you tight and call you
   sweetie pie.

(*Chorus of grunts*)

Dean If you let me kiss your hand,
I promise you I will understand,
Take care to show you my respect,
Treat you right, and hold you tight like I do with every girl
   I get.

(*More grunts*)

Dean Your silence makes me that much bolder,
I'm comin' up to kiss your shoulder,
Tanzi, as I kiss your chin,
Promise me we can live in sin.

(*Yet more grunts*)

Tanzi Dean, oh Dean, you're awful sweet,
Guess you've swept me off my feet,
I never knew, till we came together,
How much a lonely girl like me, needs a feller.

(*Grunts*)

(**Dean** *bends her over into a kiss. The* **Referee** *takes the microphone*)

Referee One, two, three, four, five, six, seven, eight, nine, ten. (*Bell*) Break! Ladies and gentlemen, in Round Five, a knockout to Dean Rebel. There will now be a fifteen minute interval while the lucky couple go off and get married and the rest of us go for a drink. Back in fifteen minutes. Thank you.

(*Interval*)

Act two

*The pianist plays a request or two. The **Referee** takes the mike and gets into the ring.*

Referee Welcome back to the continuing Trafford Tanzi story. Can I have the contestants for Round Six please, Round . . .

(**Mum** *enters sobbing her heart out*)

Referee Oh Gawd. What's the matter, Missus?

Mum Oh mister. Oh! You don't understand. I'm crying because I'm so happy. To think of it. My little girl, my Tanzi, married. (*She breaks down again*) The wedding night. The honeymoon! Oh mister, you're not a married man are you?

Referee No. No . . . I . . . er . . . I . . .

Mum You don't know what you've missed. Don't you ever have any regrets? Don't you regret it?

Referee No missus. I don't regret nothing.
No, no regrets: no, let there be no regrets,
I'd not miss, not me pint, not me ticket,
For the match on Saturdaaaay.
No, I regret nothin', no, I'll have no regrets,
No, not none, long as I'm kissing,
Some little dolly, all the day.

I've been wondering lately,
As me old age creeps along,
If I should conserve meself maybe,
Stay away from their charms,
But while I was wondering,
I knew it were useless,
They'd drag me down under,
In their loving arms.

No, no regrets: no, I won't have no regrets,
I'd not miss me morning ciggie, not me ticket,
For the betting shop on the way.
No, I regret nothin', no, I'll have no regrets,
No not none, long as I'm knowing,
There's some little girlie,
Ready to go all the waaaaaaaay.

(**Dad** *enters. They hastily disentangle themselves*)

Dad The lucky couple on their way. Just finishing off the honeymoon. What passion. That's the word for it, pulsating passion. The lot. I haven't seen anything like it since, since me own!

(**Dad** *throws himself on* **Mum**)

Dad Oh Mum!

Mum Oh Des! Des!

(*They embrace passionately*)

Referee Break it up. Break it up. This is a family show.

Mum (*Disentangles herself from* **Dad**) Those that can do! Those that can't ref!

(**Mum** *and* **Dad** *go*)

Referee Round Six. Can I have the contestants please for Round Six. And in the red corner, ladies and gentlemen, the very lovely Mrs, that lucky girl, Mrs Dean Rebel! And in the blue corner . . . (*Empty*) And in the blue corner . . . And also in the red corner, her old man, Dean Rebel. (**Tanzi** *and* **Dean** *are asleep in the red corner*) Seconds away, Round Six.

(*Bell. The* **Referee** *bounces around while* **Tanzi** *wakes up*)

Tanzi Oh! It's so early in the morning! The dew is still on the grass. What a lovely morning! The morning chorus! (*The cast oblige by making dawn chorus noises*) Oh it's so beautiful! I'm such a lucky girl. Dean's a professional wrestler now and he lets me help him train. I'm learning such a lot. He says I can write his autobiography for the *News of the World*. Listen! (*She has a notebook and pencil strung round her neck. She reads*) 'The most important part of a wrestler's career is his training.' De-ean? De-ean? Wakey-wakey. Time to get up.

Dean No. No. (*Sees* **Tanzi**) Oh yes. Yes. Oh Tanzi.

Tanzi Oh Dean.

Referee Oh Gawd!

Tanzi I've cleaned your shoes. I've ironed your towel. I've oiled the stopwatch and I've packed the knapsack with tea and sandwiches for two and the weights for the weight training.

(*She drags the knapsack over*)

Dean Good girl. I'm ready. (*He picks up the knapsack. It's very heavy*) Right, you carry the knapsack, we don't want me straining my shoulders, do we? (*He puts it on her. She staggers*) A wrestler's muscles should be flexible at all times: write that down, Tanzi.

Tanzi A wrestler's muscles . . . (*She writes it down*)

Dean Have you got the stopwatch?

Tanzi   Oh yes, Dean. (*It's round her neck*)

Dean   Good girl. Now when I say 'go' I want you – to press – the little button: on the top. Do you understand?

Tanzi   Er . . . Yes, Dean.

Dean   Right. Ready, steady: Go! (**Tanzi** *starts the watch.* **Dean** *sets off jogging round the ring.* **Tanzi** *follows*) Oh that's better. What a morning eh? Just so good to get that oxygen in yer lungs. Tanzi love, that's what all this is about. Oxygen. (**Tanzi** *is falling behind*) I feel just fantastic, you know that, Tanzi? Top of the world. Never felt better in me life. Moving like grade A well-oiled clockwork. (*He does knee bends*) Up. Down. Try it, Tanzi. (*She does and keeps doing it through this next*) Chest easy. Hamstrings cool. Tanzi, write this down: A wrestler would be nothing, nothing, without the loving support of a good woman, his wife. (**Tanzi** *writes and knee bends.* **Dean** *embraces her and they both fall over and snog*)

Referee   No contest. No contest.

(*Bell*)

Referee   Now you two, get this into your heads. The paying public don't want to know about marital bliss, they've paid their money to see the fighting. The blood and thunder. Didn't you ever beat her up, Dean? Come on, give us the dirt!

Mum   (*Outside the ring*) Beat her up? What for? My Tanzi was perfection. A credit to her mother. If there were anyone at fault it were him. Men never know when they're well off.

Dean   Come here.

Mum   What?

Dean   I said come here.

Mum   (*Going to him*) What for?

Dean   I thought so. You've got a spot just this side of yer nose. Here, let me squeeze it . . .

Mum   Well . . .

Referee   Round Seven and in the blue corner, Platinum . . . waaaaaaugh!

(**Referee, Mum** *and* **Dad** *provide backing for* **Sue**'s *song*)

Sue   Hey man,
Who's that
Funny chick?
Hey man,

                    Makes your
                    Heart beat quick.
                    Hey man,
                    And she
                    Knows a trick
                    Or two.

Backing Group Three, four, five.

Sue Hi-de hi I'm going places,
Meeting guys with famous faces,
Watch me put them through their paces
I know how the race is
Won.

Like my style and like my suntan,
Like the way my hair is done man
Pay the bills and you will see
That life is fun and fancy free
For me.

She's got the disco be-eat
She's got the disco be-eat
She's in the Beauty Business.

She can't stop,
She will bop,
Till she drops.

Hey man
That chick's
Really cool.
Hey man
See the
Fellers drool.
Hey man
And she's
Played the fool
Before.

Backing Group Five, six, seven.

Sue She's got the disco be-eat,
She's got the disco be-eat.

All She's in the Beauty Business.
She's in the Beauty Business.

Referee Seconds away, Round Seven.

Sue Tanzi pet! Lovely to see you!

Tanzi Oh. Er . . . hullo. Do I know you?

Sue Of course you do. Mind you, a lot of people don't recognise me since I went into the beauty business, funny, isn't it?

(*The* **Referee** *laughs ingratiatingly.* **Sue** *conducts him and then cuts him off*)

Sue I'm Sue, your best mate from school, remember?

Tanzi Oh yea. I do.

Sue Oh yes, it all comes flooding back, doesn't it? Little pests we were. Some of the things we used to get up to.

(**Sue** *bops. The* **Referee** *joins her*)

Sue Salami, salami,
All the boys are barmy.

Tanzi Yeah.
Sla-ate, sla-ate,
All the girls is gre-eat.

What's happened to you?

Sue You're married now, aren't you, pet?

Tanzi Yes, how did you know?

Sue Well, there's your hair (*She grabs it and pulls*) all anyhow. No make up. (*'Face bar'*) Carpet slippers. (*She stands on* **Tanzi**'*s feet and pushes her backwards*) You look like something the cat's sicked up.

Tanzi Well, I was just popping out to the shops for some tea.

Sue I wouldn't let myself go like that! I mean, you don't want him looking at anyone else, do you? Not that I don't envy you, mind. Of course I've had my chances. (*She sticks her finger in the* **Referee**'*s ear and wiggles it*) But you know my mum, she brought me up particular about marriage. (*She slaps his face*)

Tanzi I s'pose we can't all be lucky. Hey, my feller is terrific.

Sue Bit of all right? Gives you a bonus with the wages, does he? Yea, I know what you mean though, I'm in love at the moment. Ever since I turned professional with the beauty business. I carry the boards round between each round at wrestling. Well, I met this feller – middleweight – muscles all over the place. Turns me knees to jelly.

Tanzi Oh. What's his name?

Sue I'm not gonna tell you that, am I? Well, seeing as we're best mates – it's Dean.

Tanzi Dean?

Sue   Dean Rebel. Of course he's married. Got ever such a boring wife he says, possessive, y'know. Even insists on going training with him . . .

Tanzi   Noooooooo . . . (*'Irish whip: forearm smash: two-footed dropkick*)

Referee   One . . . two . . . three . . . four . . . five . . . six . . . seven . . . eight . . . nine . . . bell . . . bell . . . bell . . .

(*Bell*)

Referee   Oh there now, that was a piece of luck.

Tanzi   Why you . . .

Referee   Bad luck, I mean, Tanzi, well, saved by the bell, wasn't she? (*'Ref's hold.' The* **Referee** *'head mares' her*) And anyway, it's time you stopped living in cloud cuckoo land.

(**Tanzi** *breaks down*)

Mum   (*Climbing into the ring*) A girl needs her mother at a time like this. Tanzi, Tanzi love, come to Mum.

Tanzi   Mum . . . Mum . . .

Referee   Seconds away, Round Eight.

Mum   There, there: Mummy's here now.

Tanzi   He doesn't love me. He doesn't care. After all I've done for him. The training and . . .

Mum   There, there, now dry your eyes.

Tanzi   How could he do it? Mum, Mum, let me come home. I want to start all over again.

Mum   Tanzi duck, think.

Tanzi   Think? I am thinking.

Mum   But not along the right lines, dear. Look sweetheart, Dean may be a swine, a brutish monster but so are all men. And we love them for it. The sooner you learn the facts of life the better.

Tanzi   I hate him!

Mum   Don't say that! Remember, Dean's your husband. You promised to love and obey him.

Tanzi   I'll divorce him!

Mum   Oh you always think of yourself first, don't you? What about the disgrace to us? Your parents?

Dad   (*Out of the ring*) That's right.

Tanzi   Let me come home.

Mum   Life's not a bowl of cherries, Tanzi. You've made your bed, now lie on it. Besides, your dad can't afford to keep you.

Tanzi   I'll get a job. I'll earn my living.

Mum   Tanzi, Dean loves you in his own way.

Tanzi   Mum!

Mum   It's true! Men are like children. When they meet temptation, they succumb. That Sue may not be my cup of tea but she knows how to look after herself. You've let yourself go, my girl. Nobody wants something that looks as if it's been thrown on the rubbish tip. And anyway, what choice have you got? You've got to stand by him.

(*The* **Referee** *hands her a mike*)

Mum   Sometimes it's hard to be a woman,
Giving all your love to just one man,
You'll have bad times and he'll have good times,
Doin' the things that you don't understand.
But if you love him, you'll for-give him,
Even though he's hard to understand.
And if you love him,
Oh – be proud of him,
'Cos after all he's just a man.

(*The* **Referee** *enters in cowboy rigout. Much business*)

Mum   Stand by your man,
Give him two arms to cling to,
When nights are cold and lonely,
Stand by your man
And tell the world you love him,
Keep giving all the love you can.
Stand by your man.
Stand by your man
And show the world you love him,
Keep giving all the love you can,
Stand by your man.

Tanzi   Mum. I'll go . . . I'll go back to Dean.

Mum   That's my brave girl! You need a man to look after you at a time like this. Women are nothing alone. (**Tanzi** '*posts*' *her*) Ow! What you doing? That hurt.

Tanzi   Practising. ('*Double roll*') I'm going back to Dean, ('*Head mare*') but I'm going to work as well, (*She throws her to the ropes*) I've done all the training, and I'm going to be a wrestler as well. (*Sequence of throws ending with a 'flying tackle'. Whilst they've been fighting* **Dad** *enters*)

Dad (*Out of the ring*) Women wrestlers! Looks like something out the zoo, dunnit?

Dean Yea. And they're dirty as well. Sneaky. Like one of them little plants, they look all nice and pretty and then, snap, they've got hold of your finger. What are they called?

Referee (**Tanzi** *and* **Mum** *in a 'pinfall'*) One ... two ... three. Break.

(*Bell*)

Tanzi Venus Flytraps! Thanks, Dean. That's what I'll call it.

Referee In Round Eight, by means of a Venus Flytrap, the winner, Trafford Tanzi.

Tanzi In Blackpool and Crawley and Leicester,
The fighters are tough and are hard,
In Middlesbrough, Lincoln and Chester,
You're fighting for every damn yard,
In Newcastle, York and in Preston,
You stay on your guard.

A fighter must always be training,
A fighter must always be fit,
A fighter must always be travelling,
A fighter must never submit,
A fighter must always be working,
If she stops then she's gonna get hit.

Referee (*On the mike*) In Round Six: the winning fall by means of a Venus Flytrap, the new Northern Area Ladies Champion: Trafford Tanzi.

Tanzi You fight using headmares and armlocks.
You fight using smashes and chops,
You fight using dropkicks and headbutts,
You fight and you don't ever stop,
You fight till you're bruised and you're aching,
You fight till you drop.
A fighter must always be ... *etc.*

Referee In Round Five: her opponent is unable to continue! The winner by means of a Venus Flytrap: the new British Ladies Champion: Trafford Tanzi.

Tanzi A fighter must always be (... *etc*)

Referee In Round Two, by means of a Venus Flytrap, will you welcome please, the new European Ladies Champion: Trafford Tanzi!

(**Tanzi** *takes a skipping rope from a corner and goes into a fancy training routine.*
Dad *climbs into the ring with a large Mothering Sunday card*)

Dad   Well done, Tanzi. Never knew you had it in you. You've made your old Dad proud. Fancy becoming European Ladies Champion after only one season. Fancy that! (*He catches the rope to stop her skipping*) Now look, Tanzi. (*She starts again and he has to join in*) I know you're very busy but just stick your marker on this. It's a Mothering Sunday card. I know you want to make it up with your Mother and it's the little things that count. I'm sure you wouldn't want her to feel neglected in your hour of triumph.

(**Dad** *stops skipping.* **Tanzi** *has to stop*)

Tanzi   Oh. Ta Dad (*She signs the card*)

Dad   Right. I'll see she gets it.

Tanzi   Ta.

Dad   No, no, don't mention it. After all, I'm only too glad to be of use.

Tanzi   Wait a minute: we've had Mothering Sunday.

Dad   Have we? Oh well never mind, it'll do for next year. (*He starts to climb out of the ring*)

Tanzi   Hold on. (*She grabs the top rope and pulls:* **Dad** *somersaults back into the ring*)

Referee   Round Nine, and in the blue corner: Tanzi's manager.

Tanzi   Manager? I haven't got a Manager.

Dad   (*Pulling the contract out of the middle of the card*) Listen to the Ref, Tanzi. He knows what he's talking about. I'm your manager now. And I've got the paper to prove it.

Referee   Seconds away, Round Nine.

(*Bell. They circle.* **Tanzi** *stamps and changes direction through this next*)

Tanzi   Don't be soft, Dad, I'm over twenty-one.

Dad   No, look, here's your marker.

Tanzi   But you said that was a Mothering Sunday card.

Dad   Well, in a way it is, love. Your mother'll be made up when she hears the terms. Most thoughtful of you, Tanzi. Most generous. Fifty per cent. I couldn't have asked for better meself.

Tanzi   Dad!

Dad   Tanzi, be reasonable. After all, you're only a slip of a girl, slip of a woman. And this isn't a picnic in the park you know. This is the cut-throat world of commerce. You need someone behind you you can trust. Otherwise there'll be blood all over the place. And anyway, I've already fixed up your next fight. Mud wrestling. In Hamburg. Naked. We'll make a fortune.

Tanzi   Right!

(*'Ref's hold.'* **Tanzi** *gets* **Dad** *in a 'backhammer'. She takes the contract and 'head mares'* **Dad** *with his arm still in the 'backhammer'*)

Tanzi   (*Ripping up the contract*) This is what I think of your contract, Dad. (*She scatters pieces of contract on him. Ropes* **Dad** *and 'flying tackle'. Bell*)

Dad   But Tanzi . . . please . . . I'm your old dad. I'm family. And what about your mum? I've got to support her.

Tanzi   Tough bananas, Dad. (*She 'dropkicks' him out of the ring*)

Referee   In Round Nine, her father is unable to continue. Ladies and gentlemen, Round Ten and in the blue corner, Tanzi's long-suffering husband – Dean Rebel.

(**Dean**'s *music. He interrupts it*)

Dean   Shuuuut up!

Referee   Seconds away, Round Ten.

(*Bell.* **Tanzi** *climbs into the ring*)

Dean   Hallo, Tanzi!

Tanzi   Dean!

Dean   Well. Where've you been then?

Tanzi   Training!

Dean   You're always bleeding training! Aren't I important no more, Tanzi? Tanzi?

Tanzi   Dean, I . . .

Dean   I've said I'm sorry. What more do you want? Blood?

Tanzi   Don't be . . .

Dean   Don't you bring that up again. Sue's over and done with. I love you, Tanzi. Don't you love me no more?

Tanzi   Look, if I don't train, I won't get anywhere, will I? I'll lose me title. You should try it as well.

Dean   What?

Tanzi   Training. You lost your last fight.

Dean   Well, that was arranged.

Tanzi Oh was it now? And who was always telling me he was above that sort of thing? 'A wrestler must always fight to win, Tanzi', I wrote that down. Tell you what, I think you're slipping.

Dean And whose fault's that, eh? You thought about that? Look, I come home after a hard day's work, do I find a hot meal waiting for me? No, there's a note on the table. (*He produces it and reads*) 'Your salad's in the fridge.' Well that is not how champions is maintained, y'know.

Tanzi Oh that's what I'm s'posed to be, is it? A serving unit? Anyway, salads is good for you, and if you don't like 'em, you know what you can do. Get off your backside, and you try cooking something for a change. And we could share the housework too, y'know, it's not impossible.

Dean (*Ripping up the salad note and scattering it on the floor*) Course we could. If I wanted to. But I don't, see? Why should I keep a dog and bark meself.

Tanzi What's that supposed to mean?

Dean Look, don't be more stupid than you are. Cooking, that's your job; looking after the house and that. I haven't got a sock that hasn't got a hole in it. It's embarrassing, that's what it is. I can't go round to my mother's no more. What would she say if she knew, I ask you?

Tanzi Now look; we've been through all this, and I can't do it all. No more than you can. Not the training, the fights, the travelling and that. And everything here. It's just not possible.

Dean Well, Tanzi, my love, that's all I wanted to hear, that is. If you can't do both, then you've got to do one thing or the other. We can't have no compromises, either you decide to be my wife, my old lady; y'know, do all the things, apple pie on Sundays, afternoons in bed: or off you trot. Be a lady wrestler! It's unnatural. The only place ladies should wrestle is in bed. I'll fight you there if you like.

Tanzi That's the only place you think I've got a chance?

Dean Yea. What's it to be, then?

Tanzi I don't know.

Dean Right: well I'll decide.

Tanzi No, you bleeding won't.

Dean How many times have I told you not to swear? I'm your husband. I'll decide.

Tanzi   No.

Dean   Am I gonna have to thump you?

Tanzi   No. Yes! But in the ring, and I'll tell you what, if I lose, I'll give up wrestling and be a housewife.

Dean   Hey, now you're talking.

Tanzi   But if you lose, you give up and be a housewife.

Dean   What?

Tanzi   What's the matter? Lost your bottle? Scared of losing?

Dean   No chance. Right: you're on.

(*They leave the ring*)

Referee   Gentlemen, gentlemen: ladies and gentlemen, that concludes the Trafford Tanzi story, that is it. The main event follows immediately. For the first time in any wrestling ring, a man and a woman, fighting to the finish. This will be a catchweight contest of eight five-minute rounds, two falls, two submissions or a knockout to decide the winner. In the blue corner the ever-popular Mr Dean Rebel!

(**Dean**'s *music. He enters flanked by* **Platinum Sue** *and* **Dad** *who lead chants for* **Dean.** *He climbs into the ring and does a flashy warm-up*)

Referee   In the red corner, the reigning European Ladies Champion: Trafford Tanzi.

(*Music changes to 'Ride of the Valkyrie'.* **Mum** *leads chants for* **Tanzi**)

Referee   And remember, ladies and gentlemen, the loser of tonight's contest has agreed to quit the wrestling ring and become a housewife.

(*He calls them together and gives them the chat, examines hands and boots.* **Sue** *carries round a board with Round One written on it*)

Referee   Seconds away, Round One.

(*Bell. Throughout the fight,* **Mum, Dad** *and* **Sue** *chant and counter-chant, exchange insults, encourage and abuse the audience etc, particularly between the rounds*

Dean *and* **Tanzi** *to centre of ring: 'Ref's hold',* **Dean** *puts a 'full Nelson' on her. Kisses her neck. She jerks her arms backwards and breaks free. They circle. 'Ref's hold'.* **Dean** *puts* **Tanzi** *in a 'wristlock'. Kisses his way up her arm. She turns the 'wristlock', steps through his hands and breaks out.*

Tanzi *'Irish whips'* **Dean**: *he does a 'head spring' and lands on his feet. Claps derisively*)

Tanzi   Come on, you.

(**Dean** *throws* **Tanzi** *to the ropes, catches her in a 'bear hug' as she comes off them. Squeezes*)

        Dean   I like it, I like it.

(**Tanzi** *forces his head back until he's on his knees, jerks his head back and stamps and then throws him down face-first*)

        Referee   One . . . two . . .

(**Dean** *up. They lock hands. He forces her back to the ground to a 'pinfall' position*)

        Referee   One . . . two . . .

(**Tanzi** *gets one shoulder off.* **Dean** *forces it back again*)

        Referee   One . . . two . . .

(**Tanzi** *'bridges'.* **Dean** *climbs on top.* **Tanzi** *holds 'bridge'.* **Dean** *jumps up and lands on the 'bridge'. 'Bridge' holds,* **Dean** *jumps again.* **Tanzi** *'unbridges' and catches him in a 'body scissors' on his way down. Squeezes.* **Dean** *turns so he is sitting with his back to her. Forces her backwards.* **Tanzi** *slams him back. Forces again.* **Tanzi** *slams again.* **Dean** *twists to side, struggles one arm through her legs. Then the other. Wriggles through till only his head is in the 'scissors'.* **Tanzi** *stops him with a hand under his chin.* **Dean** *'bridges' and slips out. 'Criss cross.'* **Tanzi** *runs to the ropes.* **Dean** *runs the other way. They run back and forth.* **Tanzi** *drops flat in the middle of the ring,* **Dean** *jumps over her, bounces off ropes into a 'head butt'.* **Dean** *goes down*)

        Referee   One . . . two . . . three . . . four . . .

(**Dean** *up.* **Tanzi** *sends him to the ropes again. Goes for another 'head butt' but* **Dean** *dives over the top in a 'forward roll'. Catches her legs as he goes and gets her in a 'folding press'. But . . .*)

        Referee   Ropes.

(*They separate. They circle.* **Tanzi** *goes for 'Ref's hold' but* **Dean** *'claims' her leg. 'Leglock'. He applies pressure, then steps over it and jumps on it.* **Dean** *puts a 'figure four leglock' on*)

        Dean   Ask her.

        Referee   Submit?

        Tanzi   No.

(**Tanzi** *knocks his legs apart until he does the splits and falls over. They're both in agony. The* **Referee** *untangles them with difficulty.*)

Dean *'posts'* **Tanzi.** *And again. Goes for a third one, this time she steps up on post, dives round and behind him, grabs his legs and tips him backwards into a 'folding body press'*)

        Referee   One . . . two . . .

(*Bell*)

Referee   Break!

Mum   That bell was early! It was early (*. . . etc., etc., etc.*)

(**Dean** *and* **Tanzi** *go to their corners. Towels and drinks are brought to them.* **Sue** *carries a board with Round Two on it*)

Referee   Seconds away, Round Two.

(*Bell*)

('*Ref's hold'.* **Tanzi** *puts* **Dean** *in a 'Jap stranglehold'. He forces it off and puts it on her. She tries to force it off one way,* **Dean** *wrenches it back on. She tries the other way, he wrenches it back on again. She 'undresses' it, wriggles through, steps out of it and puts it back on him. He 'undresses' it, wriggles out but as he steps out of it, she pulls his arm up into his groin and jerks him round the ring by it*)

Referee   Break . . . break . . . break!

(**Tanzi** *eventually lets go.* **Dean** *drops. The* **Referee** *lectures* **Tanzi**

Dean *gets up.*

Dean *'arm rolls'* **Tanzi** *fast and hard. Twice. Then 'Ref's hold' into a 'full Nelson', spins her out into a 'head mare'. 'Ref's hold',* **Tanzi** *puts an 'armlock' on.* **Dean** *tries to 'forward roll' out.* **Tanzi** *forces him back to ground.* **Dean** *'neck springs' up and out, twists and 'Irish whips' her.* **Tanzi** *sends him to ropes and 'cross buttocks' him as he comes off. 'Ref's hold.'* **Dean** *puts a 'backhammer' on* **Tanzi. Tanzi** *'back somersaults' out and grips him round waist. He flails behind him. One way, then the other. She pokes a foot between his legs. He goes for it but she grabs his hands through her legs, flirts him over. His legs come up, she threads hers through. 'bridges' backwards*)

Referee   One . . . two . . . three. Break! (*Bell*) In Round Two, the first fall, by means of a bridged folding bodypress, to Trafford Tanzi!

(**Sue** *slags* **Dean** *off rotten.* **Dad** *changes sides.* **Sue** *carries Round Three board round*)

Referee   Seconds away, Round Three.

(*Bell*)

Dean   Right Tanzi, you asked for this.

Tanzi   Come on, fight fair. (*She offers handshake.* **Dean** *takes it and 'arm wrenches'*)

('*Head mares' her twice. Hard. She lands badly.* **Dean** *'posts' her and follows in with 'forearms smash'. 'Posts' her the other side. Follows in with two 'forearm smashes'. Second one illegal. The* **Referee** *talks to him.*

Dean *picks her up and 'body slams' her. She gets up. He 'forearm smashes' her twice. Second one illegal. The* **Referee** *talks to him.*

Tanzi *gets up. 'Ref's hold.'* **Tanzi** *puts a 'headlock' on.* **Dean** *lifts her up and 'knee drops' her. Kicks her in the back when she's down. The* **Referee** *talks to him.* **Tanzi** *gets up.* **Dean** *'forearm smashes' her back into the corner and goes beserk. Six or seven smashes while she's in the corner and the* **Referee** *is trying to pull him off. Eventually does so)*

> **Referee**   (*On the mike*) In Round Three, a first public warning to Dean Rebel.

(Tanzi *goes for 'Ref's hold',* **Dean** *'claims' leg. Turns her over and puts a 'single leg Boston' on)*

> **Dean**   Ask her.
>
> **Referee**   Submit?
>
> **Tanzi**   No

(Dean *puts a 'full Boston' on)*

> **Dean**   Ask her.
>
> **Referee**   Submit?
>
> **Tanzi**   No . . . no . . .

(Tanzi *pushes up with her hands.* **Dean** *sits back and forces her down again.* **Tanzi** *pushes up again. Flicks her legs,* **Dean** *'forward' rolls out.* **Tanzi** *lies prone. The* **Referee** *counts to eight.* **Tanzi** *gets up.*

Dean *'posts' her and goes beserk again. The* **Referee** *eventually pulls him off.* **Dad** *tries to climb into the ring.* **Dean** *smashes him out)*

> **Referee**   In Round Three a second and final public warning to Dean Rebel.

(Tanzi *gets up.* **Dean** *lifts her into a 'backbreaker'. Stamps)*

> **Tanzi**   Yes . . . yes . . . yes . . .

(*Bell.* **Dean** *still stamping it on. Eventually drops her)*

> **Referee**   In Round Three, by means of a backbreaker, an equalising submission to Dean Rebel.

(Mum *works on* **Tanzi's** *back.* **Dad** *complains she should be looking after him.* **Sue** *carries Round Four board round)*

> **Referee**   Seconds away, Round Four.

(Dean *goes for 'Ref's hold',* **Tanzi** *'claims' leg.* **Dean** *goes down.* **Tanzi** *sits down with her feet forcing his legs apart. Bashes on her own knees to force his legs wider.* **Dean** *yells. He offers a hand.* **Tanzi** *takes it and heaves, stretching him wider, and wider.* **Tanzi** *holds one of his legs. Marks the canvas with finger to show how wide she's going to stretch him, stands up and throws herself backwards with one leg whilst standing on the other.* **Dean** *is in agony. Eventually he gets up.*

They lock hands. He takes her hands down to the canvas. Treads on one while he turns her into an 'armstretch'. She somersaults out forwards and 'stomach throws' him over the top of her. They both lie prone)

Referee One . . . two . . . three . . . four . . . five . . . six . . . seven . . .

(**Dean** *gets up first.* **Tanzi** *follows and* **Dean** *lifts her into another 'backbreaker' as she's getting up*)

Referee Submit?

Tanzi No . . . no . . . no . . .

(*She 'bicycles' out. Throws him to ropes and 'cross buttocks' him as he comes off.* **Dean** *takes count as* **Tanzi** *climbs up ropes at corner post till she's standing on top.* **Dean** *groggily gets to his feet*)

Tanzi Shall I? Shall I?

(*She jumps from top rope in 'flying tackle'. Lands across* **Dean**'s *shoulders and they fall backwards, him underneath*)

Referee One . . . two . . . three. Break.

(*Bell*)

Referee In Round Four, a second and winning fall to Trafford Tanzi by means of a Venus Flytrap. The winner: Trafford Tanzi!

(*Everyone goes bananas and then leaves the ring except for the* **Referee** *and* **Dean**. *Music: Valkyrie*)

Referee And a big hand for the gallant loser and soon to be housewife. Mr Dean . . .

Dean (*Grabbing the mike*) Tanzi! Tanzi, I wanna rematch. I wanna rematch . . . (*He goes. The* **Referee** *takes the mike back*)

Referee Thank you, ladies and gentlemen, that concludes this evening's entertainment, if you'd like to show your appreciation for all tonight's contestants. Thank you. Thank you.

(*Music: Entry of the Gladiators as they whip in and take a quick bow*)

ACTIVITIES

The Wrestler

Tanzi Triumphs!

Dean Rebel Loses Battle of the Sexes

Trafford Tanzi, the European Women's Champion, beat her own husband, Dean Rebel, in a grudge match at the Stadium last night.

After several bouts of domestic argument Dean and Tanzi decided to sort out their differences where they both feel at home – in the wrestling ring. The winner, they agreed, was to carry on with his or her wrestling career whilst the loser was to stay at home and look after the house.

It now looks as though Dean will be tying up apron strings rather than wrestling boots. Fight fans can look forward to more stunning victories from Trafford Tanzi with her amazing Venus Fly Trap.

Speaking after the match, Tanzi said, 'My whole life has been a fight against prejudice towards me as a woman. It's great to win this victory in so public a way.' Tanzi also said that she is thinking of forming a tag-team with her former arch rival Platinum Sue early next year.

Trafford Tanzi and her Mum at the end of the fight last night

Dean Rebel, whose career has been on the decline recently, did not seem too pleased at the result. He received two public warnings during the bout itself and 'I want a re-match!' was his only comment afterwards. After such a defeat who can blame him?

Match Report – Page 4

Interview with Tanzi – Page 12

Angry Dean Rebel

Tanzi's Triumph

The page opposite shows how the match between Tanzi and Dean might have been reported in the press.

In small groups discuss:

a) How *The Wrestler* seems to treat winners and losers.
b) Whether this front page reflects any particular bias towards either men or women.

2 The box at the foot of this front page report refers readers to a full match report and to an interview with Trafford Tanzi.

Write one of these articles.

- If you decide to write the interview try to explore Trafford Tanzi's comment that she has been fighting against prejudice all her life.

- If you write the match report, decide beforehand what you think your paper's attitude to the two fighters might be and try to show this in the way you write your report.

Tanzi's struggle

'Sitting at the ringside [of the Liverpool Stadium] doing my 'research', I realised that instead of writing a straight storyline about a woman wrestler I could set the whole show in a wrestling ring and write about a woman growing up. I could use the wrestling as a metaphor for everything that happened to my 'heroine'. It was the perfect excuse to describe what I felt it was like to be a woman.

Claire Luckham

3 Consider the above quotation from the author. In small groups discuss:
- what areas of girls' and women's experience Claire Luckham has chosen to focus on
- whether you think there have been any changes in attitudes to women since the play was written in 1980
- whether you agree that the violence of a wrestling ring reflects the way women are treated by society.

4 Carry out some research about women in the UK today. For instance, you could find out: how many women MPs there are; how many women there are in top managerial positions in UK industry; the average earnings of women compared to men; the number of women taking up tertiary education; the division of domestic labour between men and women, etc. Use your findings to prepare a report on the equality of the sexes. Try to explain your findings.

The Characters

The characters in *Trafford Tanzi* are clearly meant to be larger than life. They express a number of (often conflicting) ideas. These pages offer an opportunity for you to explore the attitudes expressed by the characters in the play.

Dad

Before you begin this activity you should:

1 Appoint one member of your class to study the role of Tanzi's Dad in his or her own time.

2 The rest of the class should divide into four groups and look carefully at the attitudes he expresses in the quotations printed below. (You should also look at the scenes in which they occur.) Each group should prepare three or four questions they wish to ask Dad.

> Tanzi, Tanzi: Buttercups and Tanzi,
> She was so beautiful as she grew;
> Little frocks and cotton socks, pretty as a chocolate box,
> My little girl with eyes of blue.
>
> *Round 2*

> … say yes and I'll forget all about you wanting a career. Right? Give you fifty quid. Fifty notes, to spend on yourself. Get the lot. Nice outfit, make-up. Get yourself a decent feller. One that'll want to marry you, not fiddle about with you up them back alleys. Come on. It's all your Mum and Dad ever wanted.
>
> *Round 4*

> Women wrestlers! Looks like something out of the zoo, dunnit?
>
> *Round 8*

> And anyway, I've already fixed up your next fight. Mud wrestling. In Hamburg. Naked. We'll make a fortune.
>
> *Round 9*

3 When the class has prepared Dad's role and the questions, the person chosen to study Dad's character should sit in the centre of a circle and answer the questions asked by the groups as if she or he were Dad.

4 In Round 9 Dad seems to wish to exploit his daughter's success. One way to do this would be to sell his 'story' to a newspaper.

Write an article for a newspaper about Tanzi's childhood and success from Dad's point of view. You could present this as an interview or as a 'my own story' type of article. Do you think Dad would be completely honest about his opinions and actions?

Mum

Mum sings the song *Stand By Your Man* as a piece of advice to Tanzi in Round 8. Re-read this, or better still, listen to the version of it sung by Tammy Wynette and consider the attitude towards men that Mum expresses.

The song contains the lines

'Cos after all he's just a man.

In Round 1 (page 2) Mum begins a speech

And men are wonderful, aren't they?

5 In groups of four, divide into pairs. One pair should look through the play and collect evidence in which Mum expresses the attitude that men are wonderful. The other pair should look for evidence of Mum's opinion that men are weak. Each pair should jot down its findings.

6 As a whole group discuss the differences between your findings. What do Mum's actions towards Dad, the Ref and Dr Grope show about her attitude to men?

7 Clearly the song *Stand By Your Man* does not fully express Mum's thoughts and feelings about men. Write a further song or poem for her that explores a different aspect of her views about men.

MUM – Sara West

DAD – Tim Perrin

From the production at The Dukes Theatre, Lancaster, October 1990

The Referee

> **Referee** *n* the umpire or judge in any of various sporting events ... responsible for ensuring fair play according to the rules.

What he does

The Referee is in charge of all of the wrestling bouts in the play except for the one in which he takes on the role of Dr Grope.

 In groups quickly go through the play and try to decide on the following points.
- Is he fair?
- How well do you think he applies the rules of wrestling?
- What, if anything, influences his decision-making?
- How does he behave towards the other characters?
- Is there any difference in his behaviour in the final wrestling match?

His attitudes

2 In small groups look closely at the song that the Referee sings in Round 6. What sort of life does the Referee lead? Does the song reflect his behaviour in the rest of the play?

3 Try to decide what the Referee's attitude to women, other men, and the sport of wrestling are. Compare your decisions with those of another group.

4 The Referee is also the narrator of the story. Examine the beginnings and endings of each bout closely and see if you can detect any evidence of bias. Try to account for your findings.

The Referee on trial

5 The Referee has been accused of bringing wrestling into disrepute. He is to face a tribunal at the British Board of Wrestling, charged with sexual bias, misuse of the bell, and insufficient discipline and control during a match.

Divide your class in the following manner:

- Three members of the tribunal
- Six people to take the part of the characters from the play (excluding Dr Grope of course)
- One defender
- One accuser
- Two groups who will prepare the cases for and against the Referee and advise the accuser and defender.

Everyone should study the relevant sections of the play before the tribunal is held. At the tribunal all the characters should give evidence but only the members of the panel, the accuser and the defender may ask questions. When all the evidence has been heard the tribunal should decide whether the Referee should be allowed to keep his job.

6 Write two brief reports on the tribunal. One should be for the *Proceedings of The British Board of Wrestling*, a very serious and accurate journal. The other should be for *The Wrestler*, a popular and irreverent newspaper.

THE REF – Phil Hearne   PLATINUM SUE – Andrea Mason

From the production at The Dukes Theatre, Lancaster, October 1990

The Referee as Dr Grope

The Referee takes on the role of Dr Grope, the school psychiatrist, in Round 3. Tanzi is sent to him because she is not making progress in reading. Dr Grope discovers, however, that she can read but will not read as he wishes her to.

7 In groups look closely at Round 3 and the way Dr Grope behaves. How do you think school psychiatrists are supposed to behave? Why do you think Dr Grope treats Tanzi as if she were stupid? How does his behaviour change when he discovers that she will not read as he wishes?

8 As Dr Grope write a brief report on your interview with Tanzi Green, giving your opinion of her reading ability and her general behaviour.

9 In groups, discuss why you think the author has chosen to make the characters 'in charge' in the play (the Referee/Dr Grope) so unpleasant.

10 Imagine you are an actor who has played the role of the Referee in *Trafford Tanzi*. Write a letter to a fellow actor who is about to take on the part. What advice would you give about the Referee's character? How might your colleague try to make Dr Grope seem different? How should he conduct himself as the narrator?

Wrestling Holds

Almost all productions of *Trafford Tanzi* have employed a professional wrestler to coach the actors. One such wrestler, John Kenney, stresses the difference between reality and acting and tries to teach the actors all the professional moves without some of the pain that generally accompanies a professional fight.

Illustrated below are some of the professional wrestling holds used in *Trafford Tanzi*.

Two footed drop kick

Head mare

Body slam

Bridge

Aeroplane spin

Scissors

Scissors

Boston crab

1 Tanzi's success was partly built on her own special hold, the 'Venus Fly Trap' (see p. 22). As it was a winning hold it must have involved pinning her opponent's shoulders to the floor. In pairs talk about what you think its name suggests and what it might have involved. Attempt to produce a sketch of it.

Staging *Trafford Tanzi*

The stage directions for *Trafford Tanzi* simply say that the play takes place in a 'wrestling ring'. At various points in the play costume changes and props are suggested. If you were responsible for putting on a production of *Trafford Tanzi* you would have to decide where you were going to stage it, and how you were going to organise your costumes, props and lighting. These pages invite you to consider some of these issues.

Choosing a venue

 In groups of four imagine that you have to choose between two possible venues for a production of *Trafford Tanzi*. The venues are:

a) A wrestling ring.

b) A theatre with a thrust stage.

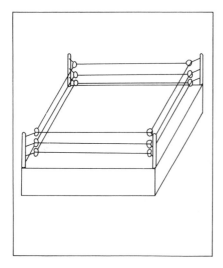

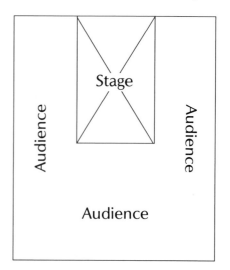

You should consider the advantages and disadvantages of each location and give reasons for your final decision. You may want to think about such points as atmosphere; accoustics (whether the actors can be heard); where your characters will stand when they are not involved in the action; where your piano and player will be; where you will store any props and costumes; how audiences might feel about each venue.

Designing a production

'Design covers all the visual aspects of a production. These usually mean the set, costumes and props, lighting and makeup. However, programmes, tickets, advertising and foyer displays would ideally be part of an overall design concept.

In working on the design for a play the director needs to think about three different kinds of visual material.

> *Functional things* – physically required by the play
> *Supportive things* – not actually physically required for the action but making it more accessible to the audience, helping the actors' performances, and building up atmosphere.
> *Decorative things* – not essential to atmosphere or action but adding extra depth to the audience's experience.

The three questions which a director needs to ask when designing a play are therefore:

> What do the actors physically need?
> What will help them?
> What will help the audience?'
>
> Adapted from *Acting and Stagecraft Made Simple*, Derek Bowskill, Heinemann

In *Trafford Tanzi* one design option would be to use only minimal props and costumes and use mime to create the necessary visual impressions.

2 In your groups discuss what would be the advantages and disadvantages of this approach.

3 As a group discuss what visual impressions you want to create with costumes and props. (Do you want to use any particular colours? Do you want to use realistic things or do you want to use, for example, larger-than-life objects and 'over-the-top' costumes? Do you want to use simple objects and costumes to 'represent' something more complex (for example an outsize nappy to suggest Tanzi's babyhood)?

4 Now divide into two pairs. One pair should go through the play listing all the props which are necessary and any you would like to add. Make notes (including sketches if you like) about what each object will look like. The other pair should go through the play considering what costumes Tanzi will wear at each point. Again make notes and sketches to show what you have in mind. (Remember, your lists should reflect the decisions your group made in activity 3.)

5 As a group of four briefly look at what the other pair has decided and make any changes you feel necessary. Then join with another group and see how your lists of props and costumes compare. Discuss the similarities and differences.

Lighting

Lighting can be used to create atmosphere and to direct the audience's attention to different parts of the stage.

6 In groups look carefully at Round 8 and decide how you might light it. You should consider: whether to light all or part of the stage; how bright the lighting should be at any point; whether to use a fixed or a moving spotlight; when lighting changes should occur. Make notes of your decisions and then compare them with those of another group.

Trafford Tanzi – Changing the Medium

Many plays have been transformed into successful film, television, or radio scripts or have even occasionally appeared later as novels. Often this means 'opening out' the story by adding extra scenes or supplying details that it was not possible to include within the timescale and location of a theatre.

Do you think *Trafford Tanzi* could survive this process?

Radio Times

Tuesday

BBC 2

9.00 Trafford Tanzi. Claire Luckham's everyday story of wrestling folk continues

Trafford Tanzi

a novel

Claire Luckham

Keystone Productions

Trafford Tanzi

The epic saga

Fight for the right to fight

Starring

Toyah Wilcox   Sting

directed by David Putnam
written by Claire Luckham

Keep Trafford Tanzi on the stage

1 Briefly consider the possibilities of adapting *Trafford Tanzi* for the screen or page.
- What could you do that Claire Luckham has not been able to do?
- What would be gained?
- What would be lost?

2 a) If you think *Trafford Tanzi* is adaptable to any other medium write a letter to a film, television or radio production company, or to a publisher, explaining your plans for adaptation.

b) If you think *Trafford Tanzi* is *not* suitable for adaptation write a letter to Claire Luckham explaining why you think she should not grant copyright to anyone wishing to adapt *Trafford Tanzi*.

Trafford Tanzi *in the classroom*

If parts of *Trafford Tanzi* are to be produced in the classroom it would clearly be too dangerous to stage the play as Claire Luckham intended it. (Unless your English teacher is also a professional wrestler!)

3 In small groups choose one round from the *Trafford Tanzi* story and discuss how you might bring it to life in the classroom. You could consider some of the following ideas:
- a series of linked tableaux or 'statues' illustrating parts of the action. Some members of a group could form the statues whilst others read out the dialogue
- a tape recording making use of sound effects and tone of voice to suggest the violent action of the play
- a video recording which used sound effects and tone of voice recorded over shots of photographs or sketches of wrestlers.

Language in Motion

1   In groups of four look carefully at the passage below. Whilst sitting at your desks one person should read out Tanzi's lines and another should read out Dad's. One person should read out the stage directions to give an idea of the actions taking place.

Tanzi   But Dad …

Dad   And don't you 'but Dad' me either. I know where you've been going after school, don't think I don't. Girls! (*'Crutch hold' and lifts her up into an 'aeroplane spin'*) What else is there for them to do except go sneaking around in the dark with lads. Disgusting, I call it. Makes me all hot inside thinking about it. In the back alleys, round the back of garages. On the railway banks. Never mind they give you those badges: 'I don't play on the railway'. No. But we do, don't we? (**Dad** *has overdone the 'spin' and now staggers to his knees*) I've seen you waiting behind Oxford Road Station and …

(*He throws her off with a 'body slam', retreats into a corner and splashes.* **Tanzi** *rolls out from under it.* **Dad** *lies prone*)

Dad   Ooh-er … Tanzi … how can you do it to you poor old Dad.

Tanzi   (*Going to him*) Dad, Dad, I didn't mean to upset you.

Dad   (*Grabbing her foot and bringing her down. 'Ankle lock'*) There, I knew it! Filth. You've been having filth.

Tanzi   No, no, Dad.

Dad   (*Applying pressure to various 'leglocks'*) Say 'yes', will you, girl? Say yes and put me out of me misery. Tell you what, say yes and I'll forget all about you wanting a career. Right? Give you fifty quid. Fifty notes, to spend on yourself. Get the lot. Nice outfit, make-up. Get yourself a decent feller. One that'll want to marry you, not fiddle about with you up them back alleys. Come on. It's all your Mum and Dad ever wanted.

Tanzi   But it would be the same as up them alleys except I'd be married. (*She tries to raise her head through this next but* **Dad** *keeps slamming it back*) I don't want to get married. (*Slam*) I want me independence. (*Slam*) I want to be somebody! (*Slam*)

Dad   Somebody! A slut, the way you're going on. A wife is somebody, isn't she? Are you saying your mother isn't somebody? Somebody? Marriage is the best career money can buy.

> **Tanzi**   I want some exams
>
> **Dad**   (*Trying to turn her over into a 'Boston crab'*) Filthy bits of
>   paper! Right! You want exams. You pay for 'em. (*'Boston
>   crab'*) You earn your own living. See how you like that.
>   (*He sits back*)

2 Read out the passage again but this time try to read it as expressively as
possible. Do not read out the stage directions this time but try to suggest
what might be happening through your tone of voice.

3 Find a space in your classroom and arrange yourselves as in the diagram
below.

Read the passage out a third time. As you do so, **Dad** should try to approach
Tanzi as vigorously as possible – perhaps by dodging, perhaps by steady
movement forward. The two people acting as shields should try to prevent
this by moving constantly in front of **Dad** but without actually touching him
or her.

Discuss the following points:
a) What differences did you notice between the three readings?
b) Was the third reading more or less expressive than the second?
c) Did you notice any change of pace in **Dad**'s movement in the third
   reading? When did these occur?
d) Which of the three readings seemed to you to reflect the meaning of the
   play most accurately?

4 A dialogue taking place in a wrestling ring is an extreme case of how
movement and meaning go together. In pairs, improvise a dialogue which
contains both these elements; perhaps a conversation while dancing at a
disco or the talk which might take place as two people climb a mountain.
Each pair should choose a different situation. When you have done this, see
if it is possible to swap the dialogue and the situation round, so that you
have a disco style of conversation on a mountain or vice versa.

Discuss the following points:

a) How does the situation you have chosen affect the conversation?
b) Does your dialogue still make sense out of its original context?
c) What problems would you have if you tried to write down your dialogue
   in the original context as a script? What would you need to add?

5 Discuss how well any play script can give you an idea of the play itself. Are
some plays more suitable than others for reading in class?

Gender Stereotypes

Stereotype – a standardised image of all members of a social group.

From the very beginning of her life Tanzi was a disappointment to her mother; firstly because she was not a boy and secondly because she did not behave as her mother thought little girls should. Mum's and the other characters' views on how Tanzi should behave can be described as stereotypes.

It is worth considering how Mum's and the other character's ideas about how girls and boys should behave have been formed.

Look at the illustrations below and answer the questions on each one.

1

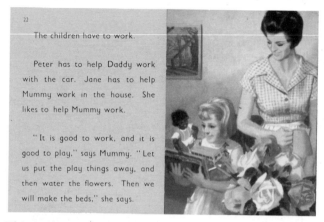

22

The children have to work.

Peter has to help Daddy work with the car. Jane has to help Mummy work in the house. She likes to help Mummy work.

"It is good to work, and it is good to play," says Mummy. "Let us put the play things away, and then water the flowers. Then we will make the beds," she says.

From: *Things we do*,
Ladybird, 1964

This is the type of book that Dr Grope forces Tanzi to read in Round 3.

a) What activities can you see in the picture? What do Mummy's and Jane's facial expressions show about their attitude to such activities? Is this confirmed by the text?

b) How true to life do you think the picture presented by the book is?

2

a) According to the makers of the cards, what are little boys like? What are little girls like?

b) Think of some seven-year-old girls and boys you know. Are they like the ones shown?

3

a) What do the magazine covers above imply about the interests of teenage girls and boys?

b) Are *all* girls interested in these things? Are *all* boys? How might girls and boys feel if they are not?

4

a) Who is the most important person in the picture opposite? How can you tell?

b) What role does this picture imply that a woman should play in a relationship?

Investigating stereotypes

5   Divide the class into two groups. One group should make a list on a large sheet of paper of as many statements as possible beginning 'Women are . . .'. The other group should make a similar list of statements beginning 'Men are . . .'. The two lists should then be displayed at the front of the class-room. As a class work through the lists and decide whether the statements are always true, sometimes true or completely false. You could also consider where each view comes from; e.g. films, television, advertising, books, etc.

6   Look back at *Trafford Tanzi*. In groups discuss: what stereotypes can you detect in the play? How many of Tanzi's problems are caused when she does not conform to a stereotype?

7   The problem with stereotypes is that they are very common and people who do not fit into them can assume that they are true for others. Write a story or play script that challenges traditional stereotypes and gives a positive image for someone who does not fit into them.

Publicity for *Trafford Tanzi*

Performances of a play can be brought to the notice of the public in many ways. One method is through the display and distribution of posters and leaflets; another is through reviews and notices in the press. Theatres are able to design, distribute and display their own publicity material, but they have no control over newspaper reviewers. The material reproduced on pages (46–9) refers to a production of *Trafford Tanzi* at the Dukes Theatre, Lancaster between 28 September and 20 October 1990.

Programmes and leaflets

1   Look carefully at the front cover of the Dukes Theatre events calendar above and the *Trafford Tanzi* poster opposite. In small groups discuss the following questions:
   a) What aspect of the play does the poster emphasise?
   b) What aspect of the play does the events calendar emphasise?
   c) Where might a poster advertising *Trafford Tanzi* be placed? What sort of people would see it?
   d) Where might events calendars be found? What sort of people might pick them up?
   e) Are there any differences between the audiences that might be attracted by the events calendar and which might be attracted by the poster? How do the calendar and poster exploit these differences?

2   Are there any aspects of the play not brought out by the poster and calendar? Design your own poster or calendar cover based on how you think *Trafford Tanzi* is best advertised.

THE DUKES · LANCASTER

DUKES PROMOTIONS WRESTLING

FRIDAY, 28th SEPTEMBER-20th OCTOBER, at 7.30 pm
FREE PREVIEW THURSDAY, 27th SEPTEMBER at 7.30 pm

TRAFFORD TANZI

A MUSICAL COMEDY BY CLAIRE LUCKHAM
★ IN A SUPER BATTLE OF THE SEXES ★

Plus Contests Between
the Following Stars

PLATINUM SUE
The Blonde Bombshell

Dynamic DEAN REBEL
Husband without a cause

DR. GROPE
The Mad Mindbender

DAD
Battling with booze all his life

MUM
Is her own worst enemy

M.D. MARK COWLING
And his Electric Upright

DIRECTOR
STEVEN OSBORNE

THRILLS · SPILLS · EXCITEMENT · MUSIC
QUEEN OF THE ACTION SPORTS

Prices: Tuesday-Friday £5.50, £3.50 Concessions · Saturday £6.75, £4.50 Concessions

MOOR LANE · LANCASTER · BOX OFFICE 0524 66645

Reviewing *Trafford Tanzi*

Information about plays can appear in newspapers in several forms.
Listings simply tell the readers when and where a play is on.

Notices give the same information as listings but add a comment on whether the play is worth going to see.

Reviews examine plays in detail and comment on such things as plot, characterisation, direction, individual actor's performances, stage design.

All three articles below refer to the Autumn 1990 production of *Trafford Tanzi* at the Dukes Theatre, Lancaster.

A

TRAFFORD TANZI
Dukes Playhouse, Lancaster

A WHOLE new dimension to the phrase "battle of the sexes" is going on in Lancaster.

Muscular men and sinewy women are grappling together in the fight to prove who is tops.

The result is Trafford Tanzi, a bizarre and hysterically funny mix of music and wrestling.

Set in the wrestling ring, Trafford Tanzi is The Dukes' latest production, which, if there is any justice in this world, will prove a winner for the theatre.

It tells the story of Tanzi's fight through life, from overcoming her mother's disappointment at giving birth to a girl rather than a boy, to a battle with her husband over her wrestling career.

Her trials, tribulations and triumphs are punctuated at various points in the action by the cast bursting into songs ranging from rock 'n' roll to the Tammy Wynette classic Stand by Your Man.

The rendition of Wynette's feminist nightmare of a song provides one of the side-splitting high points.

This show pulls no punches with its wrestling – or at least it appears not to. From where the audience sits it looks very much like the cast are going for the grunt and groan action for real.

This is very definitely theatre with a difference and one well worth going to see.

Trafford Tanzi runs until October 20.

ELAINE SINGLETON

Lancashire Evening Post

B

Wrestling – with music

TRAFFORD TANZI: Dukes Theatre, Lancaster, Friday

INTELLECTUAL eyebrows were raised at the idea of a professional theatre staging wrestling and a full-sized wrestling ring in the middle of an auditorium is certainly a surprising sight.
  But Trafford Tanzi is not just another night of grunting and groaning; it's the most amazing musical play by Claire Luckham set in the world of professional wrestling.
  The cast has learned the fundamentals of all-in wrestling from professional John Kenney, The Gypsy, and race about the ring throwing, slamming and smashing each other for nearly two hours. The odd bruised limb testifies to the hard work and pain that went into the rehearsals.
  The whole cast is excellent and Trafford Tanzi is well worth the trip to Lancaster. It runs Tuesday and Saturday until October 20 at 7.30pm.
                    HELEN WALL

North-West Evening Mail

C

Pretty violent stuff at Duke's

THE concept of staging a musical entirely within the ropes of a wrestling ring is ambitious in itself. Expecting 'wimpy' thespians to pass as convincing 'grapplers' is beginning to stretch the imagination to the limit – but sitting perilously close to the action in the Duke's Studio you very quickly become aware of the remarkable lengths to which the actors in "Trafford Tanzi" have gone to ensure realistic action.

The resulting show, for it is more a show than a piece of theatre, is not without its flaws. The weak plot structure (poor girl makes good against all the odds, confounding the male bigots and doubting females who surround her and eventually coming out on top . . . you know the sort of thing) is wholly predictable

and the Rocky style theme music that greets Tanzi's entrances is straight out of Hollywood's style book.

Black eye

Having said this the lasting impression of the performance is the incredible achievement of putting six actors into the roles of the wrestlers.

Strangely this looked less like acting than watching the professionals on World of Sport. The black eye sported by the referee (Phil Hearne) and huge bruises on the arm of Tanzi (Jan Dunn) were the real evidence of how seriously the actors were taking their roles.

It is all pretty violent stuff, expertly choreographed and frighteningly authentic we are led at breakneck speed through a retrospective look at Tanzi's formative years and see the hapless Tanzi being well and truly stepped on by all her family and friends. All this is symbolically represented by a series of wrestling bouts, which Tanzi loses.

Of course the unfortunate Tanzi eventually triumphs when she takes the men on at their own game, and

sticks one in the eye of her cheating husband when she overcomes his dirty tricks and defeats him in a wrestling match.

All this furious action is interspersed with the actors breaking into song at the drop of a hat. A splendid rendition of 'Stand by your man' is performed by Mum (Sara West) and a classic Vic Reeves-style 'No Regrets', sung by the ref, is a show highlight.

Credit must be paid to the expert guidance of wrestling tutor John Kenney, who has honed some seriously competent fighters from these actors. I wouldn't rate many people's chances against Dad (Tim Perrin) inside the ring!

The real strength lies in the incredible atmosphere created in the intimate studio, the final bout between Tanzi and Dean Rebel was truly gripping –all that was missing was an irate pensioner raining blows on the heads of the baddies with her handbag.

"Trafford Tanzi" continues until October 20.

Richard Machin

The Visitor

---

1 In groups discuss:
   a) Whether these are reviews or notices.
   b) Which article gives the most favourable opinion of the production.
   c) What aspects of the play seem to have attracted the attention of the reviewers.

2 Look closely at the comments the reviewers have made and try to decide what kind of audience they were aiming at. Support your opinion with the words of the articles. Then consider the following:
   a) Why do you think that Helen Wall says that 'intellectual eyebrows were raised' in article B?
   b) What do you think Richard Machin means when he describes *Trafford Tanzi* as 'more of a show than a piece of theatre' in article C?
   c) What does Elaine Singleton mean by 'theatre with a difference' in article A?
   d) Who do you think might be encouraged to go and see *Trafford Tanzi* after reading these reviews? Would they be regular theatre-goers or a more general audience?

3 Write two short reviews of an imaginary production of *Trafford Tanzi*. One should be aimed at regular theatre-goers; the other should attempt to interest a wider public.

Women in Sport

1 In groups jot down a list of important sporting events that take place either every year or every few years and then answer the following questions.

How many of the events you have noted involve:
a) Women and men?
b) Only women?
c) Only men?

2 Remain in your groups and jot down the names of as many sporting personalities as you can in one minute.

How many of the names you have noted are:
a) Female?
b) Male?

3 Are there any differences between the numbers of men's and women's names? Are there any differences between the numbers of female-only and male-only events? If there are, suggest some reasons for these differences.

Sportswomen in the media

- 'BBC television's *Sports Round-up of the Year, 1985* lasted 90 minutes – three minutes and 45 seconds were devoted to women.
- BBC television's 1986 programme ran over by 20 minutes to about 110 minutes – fewer than ten minutes were devoted to women, even though the public had voted the javelin thrower Fatima Whitbread runner-up BBC Sports Personality of the Year.

'Fastest woman in the world is good cook' was the headline when Fanny Blankers-Koen (nearest camera) won her unprecedented four gold medals at the London Olympics in 1948

● *Sportsweek* magazine ran an article on the heptathlete Judy Simpson which was all about how she knits sweaters for the male athletes between events. Another article on Liz Hobbs, twice world high-speed water skiing champion, focused on her sideline as a fashion model.'

Text adapted from: *Grace Under Pressure*, Adrianne Blue, Sidgwick & Jackson (1987)

● The following article appeared in *The Observer* on 23 September 1990.

Medals – but not for the admin men

Peter Nichols
suggests a fairer
deal for women

WHEN asked to nominate the male and female athletes of the year, it is always a more fulfilling exercise when one can indulge in the joys of deliberation. This year Steve Backley, after world records in Stockholm and London, was an early favourite. However, after the events in Split last month, his was not an unarguable case.

John Regis, was the sprinter of those championships; Kriss Akabusi was the most ecstatic man of the championships; and Roger Black made the comeback of the championships. Backley won the vote, but at least we had to pause for thought.

Yvonne Murray, on the other hand, took every vote bar one. There really was no choice. Murray won it last summer, after her victory in the World Cup at Barcelona, and triumphed this time as the only British woman to take a title in Split. She is following a pattern established over 20 years ago: that female champions in British athletics arrive unaccompanied – Lillian Board in 1969, Mary Peters in 1972, Tessa Sanderson in 1984, and Fatima Whitbread in 1987. If you go back to 1964, you can find a

pair, Mary Rand and Ann Packer, but that's an awfully long time ago.

After the championships, as the accolades were pouring in for the men's team, Joan Allison, the women's team manager, unfurled her indignation. Allison's anger was sparked off when she saw the TV schedule for next year's meetings. The men, she saw, were getting the televised meetings and the women were being left out.

'If the women didn't get the quality of competition,' argued Allison, 'then it was little wonder that they didn't improve.'

The outburst was widely reported and set the British Board in a dither. The agenda for the meeting of the Board's joint standing committee, held a week later in London, was amended to include an item about women's athletics, and Allison was there to present the case.

The outcome somewhat resembled a school report. Not quite 'must try harder' or 'barely up to scratch' but in much the same vein. 'The women must set their sights higher,' said the release from the Board's spokesman, Tony Ward.

Encouragement will be essential, though. Unlike the men, most women athletes still work for a living, which makes progression through the ranks difficult. In women's sport in Britain, athletics comes second only to tennis in terms of its public profile, yet the vast investment that has gone into the sport in the past six years has largely gone the way of the male athletes.

Allison's comments appear to have brought about some changes in the television timetable, although you can bet that anything approaching equality of opportunity will still be a long way off. You only have to look at the constitution of the subcommittee that has been set up to examine the weakness of women's athletics (and selected men's field events) to guess what the future holds.

Andy Norman, the promotions officer, Les Jones, the men's team manager, Dave Bedford, the International Athletes' Club chairman and Frank Dick, the national director of coaching, make up the subcommittee. There is no place for Joan Allison. There is no place for any woman. And they expect us to take it seriously?

Of the six pages devoted to sport by *The Observer* that Sunday this was the only article which even mentioned women.

 4 In pairs answer the following questions:
   a) What, according to the article, are the main differences between female and male athletics champions in this country?

b) What factors affect the relative success of female and male athletes?

c) What steps are being taken by the British Board of Athletics to improve opportunities for women athletes? Discuss whether you think they will be successful.

5 Write a letter to the British Board of Athletics suggesting ways in which the situation of women athletes might be improved. You may wish to focus on possible changes of attitudes as well as on practical matters.

FIGHTING CHANCES

Bewilderment, outrage or a salacious cackle — reactions to female boxers may differ but they are usually negative. Yet **Glenys Roberts** finds that for some, the ring is one place where a woman can stand on her own two feet

Women's boxing. The very idea brings strangled sounds to the vocal chords of the Amateur Boxing Association. These gentlemen will not go so far as to express their cynicism in words; it is 1990 and if women want to make themselves voluntary targets for flying fists, so be it. Last year, when Sue Atkins took the title from Jane Johnson from Tunbridge Wells on points, the largely male audience sidled in grinning awkwardly, not quite knowing whether to expect plain bloody amateurs fumbling around in hopeless contravention of their genes or a voyeuristic cat show.

Yet fairground booths were seen not so long ago in this country and women often fought on the booths, including Barbara Butterick, former lightweight then bantamweight champion, who is now living and training on the East Coast of America. Butterick corresponds with Atkins on the history of women's boxing – and its future. It was common for women to trail around after their fathers, brothers, uncles and to get into the ring, and

with their independence it could come again. Women who have tried it think it is a good sport for their sex, in the lighter weights, one which lends itself to their speed and bodyskills.

People who have not tried it, men and women alike, tend to think the notion is extraordinary. It is difficult to interpret the slight smile in most people's voices when the idea is put to them but it is usually salacious. Even Joyce Carol Oates, the American writer who is brilliant on the salvation-through-pain factor in men's boxing, thinks the sport is grotesque for women. Women may have been fighting, as they have, since gladiatorial times, but not without making a spectacle of themselves. Oates says it goes right against the nurturing stereotype of their sex, and therefore must be an aberrational activity, a parody, a monstrous cartoon.

There remains the question of why a woman, whose face, despite the best efforts of women's lib, is often still her fortune, would willingly put

herself in a situation where it is liable to be bashed up. Good fighters of either sex do not have their faces ruined, is Atkins's answer to that. "Does Marvin Hagler have his cheeks split? Is Sugar Ray Leonard scarred?" As to the notion that women fighters are not as other women due to some mysterious excess of testosterone, there is no easy analysis of anyone's chemical make-up as yet; suffice it to say that Atkins has a boyfriend and keen fan of 10 years. Jane Johnson is married.

Back to last year's fight. One hundred men paid £3 each to watch the two girl contenders, weighing around $9\frac{1}{2}$ stone in singlets and shorts, go the full eight rounds. Among them were Atkins's boyfriend, Barry, and her father, neither of whom boxes but both of whom support her. Mr Atkins, an ex-military man, was Master of Ceremonies for the occasion. After it was all over, upstairs in the pub, one by one the audience came up to the girls and apologised for their preconceptions. It had been a good fight and they thanked Sue and Jane for an afternoon's real entertainment. "They were proud of us."

That meant a lot. Most women, Sue says, allow themselves to cop out on life. "If the going gets tough, everyone expects a bloke to pull through, but they are amazed if a girl does the same." Out of the ring she is a good-looking girl with long streaked blonde hair and sharp blue eyes, a sense of humour and a strange air of having a different destiny. She likes to call herself "hard" and "one of the lads".

She was watching television as a child when she discovered boxing. She liked wrestling but saw very early on that it was not the real thing. It was show-business. Fun to watch, but there was no depth of character involved. She learned the names of all the real boxers and her early heroes were Jim Watt, Charlie Nash, Alan Minter. She studied their styles while herself progressing from netball and athletics to shadow boxing in the park. It was there that she met her current trainer, Horace Stopher. They were both exercising their dogs at the time – Sue's a punch-drunk collie called Bosie, after the Marquess of Queensberry's son who loved Oscar Wilde. Horace replaced as her trainer Bruce Wells, an amateur whom Sue recalls with visible admiration had some 360 fights in the Sixties and lost only two. For the time being she had to spar with the boys.

It was boyfriend Barry who first discovered a girls' boxing show in Stockwell and suggested Sue might find women opponents. Together they went to a church hall in Earls Court to find a dozen or so teenagers training for sport-fighting, a mixture of karate and judo which most were learning for self-defence. The girls have dispersed now.

Some of the girls went up North on what is called the tough girls' circuit. Tough girls will do any kind of fighting, wrestling, kicking, foxy boxing. Promoters field 10 girls of an evening, five bouts, in a pub show or night club, all willing to make a spectacle of themselves with gloves too huge to hit with and very often topless. Atkins has fought topless opponents just to get a fight, but she herself will not strip off.

This being so, she often has to go abroad to find a fight. She toured California in a caravan with the world lightweight champion, the black girl Tyger Trimiar. The girls there were fighting for purses of $2,000 but Sue could not join in because she had no licence or medical certificate. As yet no such things are needed in women's boxing here, and the biggest purse is only around £100. Atkins reckons she has spent more on boxing than she has earned: a quid a time on gym fees for starters, all subsidised by her job as a landscape gardener.

Last year, too, Atkins lost her European title to a French girl called Nancy Joseph. The girl was 21 to Sue's 29 years but that was not the problem. Nancy for all her youth had had 35 fights to Sue's 14. An inexperienced fighter loses a lot of energy in adrenalin just getting into the ring. *Le boxe* is a popular sport in France and the fight was on television, which added to Sue's dis-comfort. The referee stopped it after four rounds. The story pains our champion in the telling, as if she has not yet digested its lessons.

And that is the whole point of boxing, she says, becoming articulate as only people are who have a genuine if peculiar passion. It is one of the oldest sports and one to which one comes with few expensive encumbrances. It is way down on the list of dangerous pursuits, behind horse riding and motor racing and rugby. But none of these is the reason for doing it, still less self-defence – "Better off increasing your running speed" for that. The real reason, for all the fantasies that get the male adrenalin flowing, is that it is real.

Another woman can understand that without in the least bit wanting to get into the ring herself. It puts the contender herself into the spotlight where she stands or falls unconditionally, not as anyone's wife, or employee, dream lover or any other social role. And, in seeming to make her vulnerable as few other things do in modern life, it actually toughens her up.

Atkins says it breeds confidence and discipline and whether or not you would encourage your daughters to win their self-esteem in such a way, she thinks it a pity that those boys' clubs where Horace Stopher used to teach no longer consider it among their priorities, and positively sinful that councils such as Hackney have a doctrinal objection to boxing. "There are lots of ways of getting hurt in life. You can't not do things because of that. I had a teacher who slipped on a shiny exam floor."

Extract from *Sunday Telegraph*, 8th July 1990

 1 Why might a woman wish to become a wrestler or a boxer?

2 After reading the above article and *Trafford Tanzi*, discuss the problems women encounter in becoming wrestlers or boxers.

3 In small groups discuss how you feel about violence and violent sports being treated as entertainment.

'Cooking, that's your job' (Dean Rebel)

I Had Rather Be A Woman

I had rather be a woman
Than an earwig
But there's not much in it sometimes.
We both crawl out of bed
But there the likeness ends.
Earwigs don't have to
Feed their children,
Feed the cat,
Feed the rabbits,
Feed the dishwasher.
They don't need
Clean sheets,
Clean clothes,
Clean carpets,
A clean bill of health.
They just rummage about
In chrysanthemums.
No one expects them
To have their
Teetotal, vegetarian
Mothers-in-law
To stay for Christmas,
Or to feel a secret thrill
At the thought of extending the kitchen.
Earwigs can snap their pincers at life
And scurry about being quite irresponsible.
They enjoy an undeserved reputation
Which frightens the boldest child.
Next time I feel hysterical
I'll bite a hole in a dahlia.

Daphne Schiller

In groups discuss the following:

1 What are the frustrations of being a woman mentioned by Daphne Schiller?

2 Why does she compare herself to an earwig?

3   **Dean**   ... Cooking, that's your job; looking after the house and that. I haven't got a sock that hasn't got a hole in it. It's embarrassing, that's what it is. I can't go round to my mother's no more. What would she say if she knew, I ask you?

How is Dean's view of how Tanzi should behave similar to the role described by Daphne Schiller?

4 Which would you rather be? A housewife, an earwig or a female wrestler?

Very Simply Topping Up the Brake Fluid

Yes, love, that's why the warning light comes on. Don't
panic. Fetch some universal brake-fluid
and a five-eighths screwdriver from your toolkit
then prop the bonnet open. Go on, it won't

eat you. Now, without slicing through the fan-belt
try and slide the sharp end of the screwdriver
under the lid and push the spade connector
through its bed, go on, that's it. Now you're all right

to unscrew, no, clockwise, you see it's Russian
love, back to front, that's it. You see, it's empty.
Now, gently with your hand and I mean gently,
try and create a bit of space by pushing

the float-chamber sideways so there's room to pour,
gently does it, that's it. Try not to spill it, it's
corrosive: rusts, you know, and fill it till it's
level with the notch on the clutch reservoir.

Lovely. There's some Swarfega in the office
if you want a wash and some soft roll above
the cistern for, you know. Oh don't mind him, love,
he doesn't bite. Come here and sit down Prince. Prince!

Now, where's that bloody alternator? Managed?
Oh any time, love. I'll not charge you for that
because it's nothing of a job. If you want
us again we're in the book. Tell your husband.

Simon Armitage

1 How does the speaker in the poem try to make his female customer feel small?

2 In pairs improvise a dialogue in which a male customer asks to have the break fluid in his car topped up. What differences do you think there will be in the mechanic's approach?

3

> **Dean**   Have you got the stopwatch?
>
> **Tanzi** Oh yes, Dean. (*It's round her neck*)
>
> **Dean**   Good girl. Now when I say go I want you – to press –
> the little button: on the top. Do you understand?
>
> **Tanzi** Er ... Yes, Dean.

What set of assumptions about women do 'Very Simply Topping Up the Brake Fluid' and the quotation from *Trafford Tanzi* illustrate?

4 a) What traditionally female activities and roles should boys and men be encouraged to learn?
b) Write a story, poem or essay about what men need to learn from women.

Happily Ever After?

All My Friends Are
Married Now

hello vick how you doing
keeping o.k.?
i'm glad everything's
all right
it's ages since I've seen you
you're different now
looking a bit older
you're sure you're o.k.?
i wondered why you'd stopped writing
why you never came down
or ever got on the phone
too many other things on your mind
i can see that now
you're sure nothing's wrong?
i'm glad
for a minute you had me worried
you've put on weight
are you still doing all those things
you were doing when i knew you?
none of them? i'm surprised
you always used to like doing things
it was you that always had the ideas
yes i suppose it is different
when you settle down
do you still see. . .?
so you don't see any of them now
yes i suppose it is awkward
now you have other things
to worry about
sue asked about you
the other day
wanted to know how you were
yes i'll tell her you're fine
are you sure you won't stop
for a drink?
you have to be getting back
i understand. Surely he wouldn't mind
if you were a bit late home?
after all it's not often i see
you and you were my best friend
i wish i could persuade you to
change your mind
yes i'd love to meet him sometime
it's been nice seeing you

yes do write – come down sometime
some other time perhaps
when you aren't so busy
no i won't keep you much
longer
just one more question
ARE YOU SURE YOU'RE O.K?
ARE YOU SURE EVERYTHING IS ALL RIGHT?

Barbara Child

The Choosing

We were first equal Mary and I
with same coloured ribbons in mouse-coloured hair

and with equal shyness,
we curtseyed to the lady councillor
for copies of Collins' Children's Classics.
First equal, equally proud.

Best friends too Mary and I
a common bond in being cleverest
        (equal)
in our small school's small class.
I remember
the competition for top desk
at school service.
And my terrible fear
of her superiority at sums.

I remember the housing scheme
where we both stayed.
The same houses, different homes,
where the choices were made.

I don't know exactly why they moved,
but anyway they went.
Something about a three-apartment
and a cheaper rent.

But from the top deck of the high-school bus
I'd glimpse among the others on the corner
Mary's father, mufflered, contrasting strangely
with the elegant greyhounds by his side.
He didn't believe in high school education,
especially for girls,
or in forking out for uniforms.

Ten years later on a Saturday –
I am coming from the library –
sitting near me on the bus,
Mary
with a husband who is tall,
curly haired, has eyes
for no one else but Mary.
Her arms are round the full-shaped vase

that is her body.
Oh, you can see where the attraction lies
in Mary's life –
not that I envy her, really.

And I am coming from the library
with my arms full of books.
I think of those prizes that were ours for the taking
and wonder when the choices got made
we don't remember making.

Liz Lochead

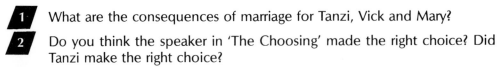

1   What are the consequences of marriage for Tanzi, Vick and Mary?

2   Do you think the speaker in 'The Choosing' made the right choice? Did
Tanzi make the right choice?

3   Write a story or poem about the consequences of an important decision.